MISSIONARY Stories

Told by AUNT THERESA

MISSIONARY STORIES

TOLD BY
AUNT THERESA WORMAN
Director of the KYB Club,
Radio station WMBI,
Chicago, Ill.

MOODY PRESS • CHICAGO

MISSIONARY STORIES
TOLD BY
AUNT THERESA

Copyright, 1948, by
The Moody Bible Institute
of Chicago

Printed in the United States of America

CONTENTS

3

NOT WORTH A CHICKEN
✦✦✦✦✦✦✦✦✦✦✦✦✦✦✦✦✦✦✦✦✦✦✦✦✦✦✦✦✦✦

I DON'T care if you are the daughter of my husband's brother," screamed big, fat Wambi as she squatted before the small fire in front of her round grass hut in Africa, "you're full of devils!"

"They're trying to get out of me, and they will, too," shouted Nyota. "See," and she pointed to an ugly, red sore on her right leg.

Nyota was one of the meanest, dirtiest girls in all Africa. She liked to be dirty and she liked to be mean. At least she thought she enjoyed it. Just once in her whole life had the thought come to her that it might be nice to be different. That was the time the two white ghosts came to their village. She knew now that they were really a white man and his wife from far across the sea; the day they had come Nyota and the other children in the village, thinking they were from the spirit world, hid in terror.

The missionaries had sung beautiful songs and spoken beautiful, never-to-be-forgotten words. Nyota and the others had finally crept out of their hiding places to listen to them. The man said the story they told was from a Book which came from heaven and was true. It was a story of a new God, new to Nyota, but known to other

5

men and women in other parts of the world for ages and ages. This God was truly an ancient One, for the white man said He had always lived.

The missionaries told, too, of this Great One's love for Nyota and her people, and said He loved them so much that He had given His only Son to die for them. If Nyota would love this God and His Son, whose name was Jesus, said the missionaries, she would live forever with Them in a beautiful, clean place called heaven. This Son, they claimed, could make bad people good.

Nyota chuckled when she heard that. "They don't know how bad I am. I wonder if even I could be made good by this powerful One?" But just then she spied a little red purse that belonged to the missionary lady and she stole it. Since then, Nyota was nowhere to be seen when the missionaries called at her village.

Nyota forgot Wambi for a moment, as she thought about the missionaries and the story they had told. "I've a good notion to tie you to a tree in the jungle and let the man-eating tiger tear the heart out of you, just like he tore the heart out of your no-good father," continued Wambi.

Nyota's heart beat a bit faster at the mention of the tiger, but she wasn't going to let her aunt see that she was afraid. "I'll run away so you'll never catch me. You can't give me to the tigers."

"Run away, foolish one, and the snake will get you. Saba told me you didn't work at all today, lazy one. He said you lay in the tall grass beside the peanut field and just looked at the sky."

"I'm not lazy; my leg hurt me," said Nyota.

"And he said you scratched and bit Matemo's little sister and stole a string of tiger's teeth. And now you've kicked over our kettle of food. What can one do with such a lazy, careless child?"

"Give her to old Mboka. He knows how to tame wild girls like her," said Saba, Wambi's son.

"Oh, no, no, don't give me to old Mboka! I'd rather have a lion tear me to little bits than to belong to that wife-beating old man. I'd rather have a snake squeeze the life out of me!"

Many were the tales in the village of the terrible things old Mboka did to the women in his kraal. The thought of belonging to him brought terror to the heart of Nyota.

"Get out of my sight quick, or I'll send Saba to tell old Mboka he can have you," said Wambi. Anger blazed in her eyes.

This wasn't the first night Nyota had been forced to stay out all night. It wasn't the first time she had gone without supper. As Saba was always fed first and he was very greedy, many nights she had only a few scraps for her supper. Nyota tossed her head in the air and walked away from Wambi's grass hut as though she were the daughter of the chief, instead of a little orphan girl whom no one wanted or cared for.

She would go to Ndombo's hut. Ndombo and his wife had swallowed the white man's religion. Their place was clean and they would share their evening meal with her. There wasn't room in their hut for her, but they'd give her a mat and let her sleep just outside their door. She'd get to see their fat baby boy, too. And maybe Ndombo's wife would teach her that song she sang to the baby. The missionary lady had taught it to her. It wasn't sad sounding like the songs everybody else sang; it was a happy little tune. Ndombo told Nyota that the songs of their people were all sad because their hearts had no hope. The Jesus religion gave people such a hope for this life and the life to come that their hearts overflowed in happy songs.

As darkness came over the land, Nyota lay on the hard

ground outside Ndombo's hut, but she could not go to sleep. Her leg hurt too much. She lay thinking of when she first came to this village three years ago. Her uncle hadn't wanted her, but he felt he had to take her in because she was his brother's child, and his brother was dead now. Wambi, his wife, had always hated her; she thought of her as just another mouth to feed. Saba, the son, was cruel to her.

Nyota felt so alone. There was no one in all the world who loved her. No one who cared whether she lived or died. No one to feed and care for her. She was kicked and beaten and yelled at from morning till night. No wonder she was mean.

Nyota believed, as all in her village believed except Ndombo and one or two others, that everybody was full of evil spirits. These evil spirits were trying to harm every person and every animal. They were even living in stones and in trees and bushes. One had to have a stout heart to sleep out in the open where the evil spirits could do with you as they pleased. So Nyota didn't enjoy the beautiful moonlight and starlight above her, or the beauty of the palm trees against the sky. She saw only evil spirits lurking about ready to pounce on her, and her heart was fearful. Poor Nyota was to be pitied!

"The evil ones are trying hard to get out of me tonight," thought Nyota as her leg ached and throbbed with pain. It was just a week ago that the witch doctor had sent for Wambi. She had found him sitting in his dark, dirty hut with all his fetishes, charms and medicines around him. "Nyota has evil spirits living in her," he said "I will call them out, but you must give me one of your chickens."

Wambi hesitated a minute. Nyota was not worth a chicken, but the witch doctor looked so cross that Wambi feared he would cast a magic spell over her if she did not give him the chicken, so she said he could have it.

That night the witch doctor crept to Wambi's hut after Nyota was asleep. He muttered strange words, with weird sounds. He waved his arms in strange motions, while Wambi and Saba looked on with bright eyes full of fear and wonder. Then he cut the skin of Nyota's right leg to let the evil spirits out. Nyota awakened with a cry of pain and fear. But Wambi told her the evil spirits could get out of her now. And Nyota, knowing there was someone stronger than herself who made her do bad things, believed that the open sore on her leg was allowing the evil spirits to leave her body.

Poor little Nyota! Although that had happened a week ago, every day since then the leg had hurt more and more, until now it was a big open wound.

Late in the night Nyota fell into a restless sleep, only to awaken at daylight burning with fever. She lay on the ground outside Ndombo's hut, moaning and saying queer things. She didn't know where she was. The infection from the leg had gone through her whole body and Nyota was a very sick girl.

On the way to his peanut field, Ndombo stopped at Wambi's hut and told her about Nyota. She said she would send Saba to carry her home.

Wambi went to the mat where Saba was sleeping and shook him. "Wake up, my son. There is something you must do and do quickly." Saba sat up on his mat and his mother came close and whispered to him, "You remember how the witch doctor had Mbangu kill their only goat and sprinkle the blood toward heaven when their son was dying. Nyota is sick, perhaps dying, and she is not worth a goat. That worthless one has already cost me a chicken. Go to Ndombo's house and pick her up. Make believe you are carrying her here, but take her to the edge of the jungle. We will say she did not know what she was doing and wandered off there by herself."

And Saba, cruel boy that he was, went to do as his mother bade him.

Nyota was so sick that she did not know when Saba picked her up. She did not know when they left the village nor when she was laid at the edge of the jungle where poisonous snakes crawled and where wild animals stalked, ever on the lookout for prey. Nyota did not hear the soft pad of tiger feet, nor did she see the gleaming yellow eyes look at her. She did not know when the tiger crouched for his spring upon her. But God in heaven saw, and not one minute too soon, not one minute too late, He had His servant walk that way.

It was the day for the missionary and his wife to visit Nyota's village. To reach it they had to walk close to the jungle for some distance. The keen eye of the white man saw the big cat intent on some object on the ground. He saw him crouch for the kill, but the white man was fast. He was carrying his gun in the crook of his arm and quick as a flash it was raised, his game sighted, the trigger pulled and the tiger rolled over dead.

Wambi and Saba were glad when the missionary took Nyota to the mission compound in a village several miles away. There she was washed till her black skin shone. Then she was put to bed on a clean mat, and for the first time in her life she had on a clean white nightgown. Proper care and love soon made her well. Her body was so starved that she thought she could never get enough of the good soup, and her heart was so starved that she thought she could never get enough love. They gave her plenty of both at the mission station.

And Nyota, who once liked to be dirty and who liked to be mean, is now one of the cleanest, sweetest girls in all Africa. If she even speaks a harsh word to anyone her heart aches until she has asked God and the person she hurt, to forgive her. So you know the blessed Holy Spirit is living within her, teaching her the things of the Lord Jesus and making Him very real to her.

She goes often to her own village to tell about the Chief of the Skies and His Son Jesus. Wambi and Saba look at her in amazement. She has such a shiny look about her. Her reading to them from a little book was like magic to them. Saba said, "Nyota knows white magic. She makes the little marks talk words." They know now that her book is the Bible, and that the same Jesus who saved her and made her a new girl wants them for His own. Saba has even been heard to say, "I wonder if God could put a shine in me like He did in Nyota." Nyota is praying for them every day, and she thinks it won't be long until Wambi and Saba will give their hearts to Jesus.

—*Aunt Theresa*

2

INDIA

"ARE YOU SHINING FOR JESUS?"

✛✛

IT WAS evening in the Village-of-the-Squirrels in south India, and Ya-hub sat cross-legged outside his mud-built home. It was the evening of the Lamp Festival, and most of the houses in the village were gay with hundreds of little lights.

"It is fine," he thought, with all an Indian boy's love of gay brightness. Just then his little sister Sabina ran out of the house.

"Oh, Brother, I'm glad we're going to see the lights on the river. It is good of Uncle Shankar taking us. Hark! I hear bells; the *tonga* (bullock cart) is coming."

A moment or two after the children had climbed into the clumsy wooden cart, off started the bullocks, jingling the bells on their necks. Inside sat Sabina talking eagerly to her little cousin Prema while Ya-hub sat on the side of the cart swinging his long legs over the edge.

Part of the way lay through jungle woods, and Ya-hub hoped he would see a panther or some such wild animal; but they were all shy that night, so he was disappointed. At last they reached the river where all the people, dressed in their best clothes, lined the banks. Eagerly they watched the tiny wooden rafts on which they had placed their little clay lamps. Each of these was lighted by a piece of cotton wick floating in a shallow saucer of oil. Gently the little rafts floated downstream, and as they were carefully balanced most of the little lamps were kept alight.

The people believed their lamps went to cheer their ancestors and dead relatives who might be groping about in the darkness of another world. The thousands of little bobbing lights on the water made a very pretty sight, but whenever one was swamped and "drowned" the owners became sad indeed.

Prema who had just begun to go to the Christian school in the village was greatly delighted.

"Oh, how much I should like a lamp sent to me if I were alone in the dark."

"But, Prema," said her little cousin, "it is only a sort of game, though these people who keep the Festival of Lamps believe that their lights somehow reach and help their lost ones. Of course, it is all useless but, you see, they don't know about God and that Jesus is the Light of the world."

"But isn't there any dark place to which people go when they die?" asked the little girl. "My Granny says so, anyway."

"Not where Jesus is," said Sabina. "Our teacher often tells us how happy her little son was when he went to be with Jesus. She, too, can smile when she thinks about him, although she has no child at all now."

Prema said no more, and in an hour or so they had to return. Indeed, they were half asleep lying in the straw at the back of the cart when they heard Ya-hub talking to his uncle.

"Say, wouldn't it be fine if we could make a lot of lamps and take them to our Children's Church, and get the *durra* (missionary) to tell all about shining for Jesus and letting others see the light through us?" Up jumped the little girls to listen as their uncle replied.

"Why, yes, that might be a bit of real witness, Ya-hub. You could all light your lamps from the big oil one on the table, and march round the church singing."

The children had a church of their very own in the village, built by their fathers and elder brothers, though they had all had a share. How they loved it, and now the thought of having a Christian festival of lamps in it pleased them well. There were many boys and girls around who never came to their happy meetings and Sunday school.

Being all very poor the children had to make and model their own little cup-like lamps out of clay. One of the Christians was a baker, so he let them put their lamps to dry out and harden in his big ovens. Being very shallow, a spoonful of oil was enough, and a scrap of twisted cotton rag or cord furnished them with the wicks.

Of course when the people saw the Christian boys and girls all gathering outside the church they were greatly interested, and as many as possible crowded inside. They squeezed together around every window to watch as the children marched around stopping to light each lamp from the big one placed on the table.

Then they formed a procession, and Ya-hub, who was very clever at making verses, had taught them this chorus to sing to a native melody.

> Always shine for Jesus
> Like a lamp so bright,
> Show to all in darkness
> He can be their Light.

Then all the little lamps were placed in the table to form a cross, and the *durra* explained and gave a simple message which the people could understand.

"It is not enough just to carry a lamp for Jesus in His house; we all, old and young, must ask Him to fill our hearts with His love so that we can shine for Him in our daily lives and actions."

Suddenly Ya-hub bowed his head, for he had just remembered something. He had been so pleased to make and carry an extra good lamp in the church; but what about Ranji—a boy whom he looked upon as his enemy? True, Ranji had told lies and got him into trouble, and was always acting mean because he was jealous of Ya-hub's ability at school.

"But he hasn't got Jesus; he has no lamp in his heart," thought Ya-hub. "I ought to forgive him and show him Jesus has made me feel different. I suppose that is how I should try to show him my lamp."

It was very, very hard, but Ya-hub bravely went and asked Ranji to forgive the angry feelings which had filled his heart toward him.

"But why do you speak such words?" said the boy in surprise. "You know I told a lie and got you into trouble."

"Yes, I know," said Ya-hub, "but I carried a lamp in our church festival last night, and I must do more than that. I must forgive you and be friendly toward you in future."

Ranji was so astonished he said no more then, but the light from Ya-hub's lamp of witness did not shine in vain.

—*Amelia O. Stott*
Used by permission of Sunday School Times, and the author.

3

CHINA

LI CHEN FINDS THE TRUE FRIEND
❖❖❖

LI CHEN was hungry. She was starving, and she was thirsty. With no water for three days, the sun seemed even hotter, and the cutting wind swept across the burning China desert. Every time Li Chen moved, she moaned. Part of the time she talked to herself, and part of the time she prayed to her ancestors.

"Honorable ones," she said, "Li Chen is suffering. She cannot stand it much longer. Please take her home to be with good ancestors."

She moaned again and tried to crawl another step. You see, Li Chen could not walk. She had never walked in all of her thirteen years. She had been born with tiny misshapen feet and always shuffled along with the aid of homemade crutches.

But in the rush to get away from the bandits, who had raided the mountain home two weeks before, her crutches were lost. Her parents had never come back for her.

So Li Chen had crawled many miles, seeking food and water. For the last three days she had crawled toward this spring. But when she arrived, she found it had dried up under the parching sun.

It was no use to move, for there was no place to go. So in despair Li Chen sank down into tired, hungry sleep. For a long time she dozed.

Then she awoke with a start. There was a roar and a long scream ringing through the skies. Looking into the fiery sun, Li Chen could dimly see a great American sky bird that carried men. The wings were made of brilliant red feathers, and the great scream came because the bird was diving toward the mountain.

"Oh, no!" Li Chen cried out, again and again. The feathers were not feathers They were plumes of flames. The great American bird was badly wounded. Out of its back sprang tufts of cotton smoke. They bloomed out into big umbrellas.

Then Li Chen could see that men were floating down to earth in safety. But the iron bird seemed to be plunging straight at her. She tried to move, but the pain was too great. With the noise of a thousand storms, the big airplane tore into the forest on the mountainside. It cut off the tops of great trees and finally stopped in the huge branches of some of the grandfather trees.

Red and yellow and orange flames blossomed forth, and the whole airplane was one great color ball. But out of that great light dropped what looked like a man, clothed in flame. In a moment he was rolling around on the ground, trying to put out his blanket of fire. After a long hard fight, the fire was out and he lay very still.

Li Chen called out in Chinese. "Hiee! Are you alive yet?"

Then in a voice that came from way down inside and must have hurt very much to talk with, she heard him answer in broken Chinese, "Yes, thank God, I am alive. But I am burned badly. Come closer and perhaps you can help me."

Li Chen tried to forget her bleeding knees and torn hands as she crawled toward the stranger. It hurt much, but finally she reached his side. "It was hard for me to get here," she explained. "I cannot walk."

"That isn't so bad," said the stranger. "I am blind."

Then she could see his face was all burned. His eyes were blistered shut. "Oh, you are badly hurt. And I cannot do you any good. I have nothing to help. And everything of yours is burned up in the thing that flies."

"There is only One that can help me now. Let's talk to Him."

Li Chen shook her head. "There is no one here. You must have hurt your head. I can see and you can't and I say there is no one here. Those other men came down on the other side of the valley, and it is two day's journey to them. There is no one here."

"Yes, He is here all right. We can talk to Him." And the stranger started talking as though there were someone right beside Li Chen.

"Lord Jesus, thank You for saving my life. I don't know why You let us crash, but there must have been a reason. Now will You give me wisdom and strength to get out safely, if it is Your will? Amen."

For a long time it was silent, and Li Chen wondered what the airman was doing. Finally he drew a deep breath. "Would you like to help me, my friend?"

"Yes," Li Chen hestitated, "but I am so small and weak, and I don't know how I could help."

"Do you have good eyes and do you know the way to the village?"

"Yes, I can see and I know the way but I cannot walk." Li Chen was about to cry with helplessness.

"Good! You be my eyes, and I will be your feet! My head and body are burned but my legs are okay. Let's go!"

The Chinese girl saw the airman grit his teeth. Great drops of sweat rolled down his face as he painfully got to his feet. He lifted her to his shoulders.

Then started the walk that they would never forget. She would tell him when to turn, to step up or step down, and they moved along on his strong legs.

To keep their minds from the terrible journey, he asked all about her home and herself. She talked until her words became a mumble, and even she did not know what she said. Dimly she could hear him talking to that unseen Friend, Whom he called Jesus. Over and over as he stumbled along, he pleaded for strength for both of them.

They stumbled into bushes, and once she was so tired that she did not even see the tree until they ran right into it. It knocked them down hard. They both lay there weeping and, in sheer weariness, fell asleep.

It seemed like ages later that they wakened and started on the endless journey again. Li Chen was not sure that they were on the right path. Nothing seemed to matter any more except to keep moving. She heard voices and thought she felt hands lifting her from the blistered back of the airman. Then she sank again into sleep.

When Li Chen awoke, she was lying in a comfortable straw bed. Someone was forcing a cold liquid between her lips. Greedily, she drank; then more sleep; then waking moments and more sleep. She did not know how long it was before she could stay awake.

Not until then did she become aware that in the bed across the room was the stranger. That is, his voice was over there. The rest of him was all wrapped in white bandages, and she couldn't see his face. But there was a smile in his voice.

"Well, He brought us out safely, didn't He?" the voice said, "Jesus, I mean."

Li Chen's lips quivered, and a little cloud appeared on her face. Then a tear drop trickled down her cheek. "I was not afraid out on the mountain, but I am afraid now. If I should die, where would I go? I have no good friend like you have. Who would take care of me?"

"Didn't Jesus save me out of the crash and the fire? Didn't He send these good people to save us? Don't you think that He could take care of you?"

"Yes I know that He could, but maybe He doesn't want to." The Chinese tears fell just as American tears do.

"Listen to what God's Book says. 'God so loved Li Chen that He gave His only begotten Son Jesus, that if Li Chen would believe on Him, she would never perish but would have everlasting life'."

Li Chen looked toward her poor crippled feet that had never walked and never would walk. She felt so heavy inside and needed someone so much. "I want Jesus with all my heart," she said. "I need Him and I want to be saved."

It didn't take long for the airman to show Li Chen the way. And she was soon smiling.

She felt a hand on her shoulder. As she turned, a nurse with golden hair kissed her on her forehead. "I'm so glad for you, Li Chen. You see, we have been praying for you since we found you. You didn't know it, but this is a missionary compound, and we are missionaries. Jesus loved you enough to send us to you." And the tears of joy started to fill her blue eyes. For a long time no one spoke.

Then the airman broke the silence. "I didn't know why God let us crash, but I do now. The great thing about having Jesus for a Friend is that He never makes a mistake. Never!"

-*Frank Waggoner, Jr.*

WE ATE THE RAFT
❖❖❖❖❖❖❖❖❖❖❖❖❖❖❖❖❖❖❖❖❖ ¡

NAN, please tell me a story," said eight-year-old Ted to his big sister, Nancy Kay. They were in their car in front of the A. & P. store while mother was doing the Friday shopping. Nan could tell wonderful stories when she wanted to.

"What story would you like to hear this time, Ted?"

"Tell me the one about the time you ate your boat." Nancy Kay smiled. She knew that was the one he'd ask for; he always did.

"Well, Ted, when I was about your age, I thought the world was about thirty miles long. That was as far as I had ever traveled. That's how far it was from where we lived in Corrville to Grandma Carlson's house. I thought that all boys and girls had nice mothers and fathers who took good care of them. That is, all except Peter Goodwin, who lived with his grandma and grandpa. And I thought everybody had schools and Sunday schools and churches. It wasn't until I was half past ten that I learned that the world is a very big place and that all boys and girls do not have fathers and mothers and nice homes. That was the year Daddy, Mother and I went to Mindanao as missionaries. We had to leave you home with Grandma because you had been ill. We got on a train—"

"Was it a streamlined train with a Diesel engine?" interrupted Ted.

"I don't remember whether it was or not. But it was a train that went very fast, and yet it took us a long time to get to the Pacific Ocean. When we arrived there, I said to Daddy, 'O Daddy, we've come to the end of the world.' He laughed and said, 'Oh, no, we haven't, Pumpkins.' He always called me that because I was round and fat and had yellowish hair when I was little.

"After we reached the ocean we boarded a big ship, and that too went very fast, but still it took us days and days to get to where we were going, an island in the Pacific Ocean. When we landed, I said to Daddy, 'Surely, we're at the end of the world now.' But he just smiled and said, 'No, Pumpkins, there's more world than this.' Then we took an airplane.

"A big super-fortress with twin engines?" asked Ted.

"No, it was a small plane, just big enough for the pilot, Mother, Daddy, and me. When we landed on the little strip of cleared ground not far from the mission, one of the natives, who had seen only big passenger planes, thought our plane was so small that he said, 'O look at the child of the big bird.' They always called airplanes birds.

"Life on Mindanao was new and wonderful. I'd always lived in a little town in the United States. There I lived in a bamboo house right on the edge of the jungle. I was the only white girl in the little school and the church. It was beautiful and peaceful and lovely where we lived, Ted. At night the moon shone brighter than the moon had ever shone at home, and I'd lie awake for a long time looking at it and listening to the jungle sounds. I wish you could have heard the birds—how they did squeal and squawk and make all kinds of noises. They frightened me dreadfully at first, but I got used to them after a while.

"Mother fixed up our house very nice, and we had plenty of good food to eat. I felt so safe and secure. Daddy was big and strong and the Christian natives just loved him. They helped him build a bamboo church, and on Sundays they would come to church singing and carrying armfuls of flowers. The inside of the church looked like a flower garden.

"It was so nice there, Ted, until the night that old Juan came to our door with terror in his eyes. We were having devotions and I was praying. I remember my little dog Snooky was curled up right beside me. She was always very quiet when we prayed. All of a sudden there was a loud pounding on the door and old Juan burst into the room. He'd been running and his voice came in gasps. 'Make no delay, man of God. Take the wife and child and flee for your lives. Even now the enemy is at the edge of our village. Go into the jungle and hide. All the village is fleeing.' Then he was gone.

"Mother grabbed me by the hand. I tried to snatch up Snooky, but mother pulled me toward the door. Poor little Snooky! I never saw her again. Mother, Daddy and I ran as fast as we could into the jungle. We didn't have time to get any food or to take any extra things. All night long we crept slowly through the jungle, and when daylight came, Daddy made us hide in some thick underbrush. Again at night, we traveled on. Daddy said we were heading toward the sea, where perhaps a submarine crew would pick us up."

"You were hungry, weren't you, Nan?"

"Hungry? Teddy, I was starved. On one of our rest stops I fell asleep and dreamed that I was so tired and hungry I couldn't walk another step. All of a sudden I came to a big mountain. It was made of oatmeal. I'd never cared for oatmeal, but I started nibbling at the mountain just like a little mouse. My, it was good! I was having such a good time, and then I woke up.

"How I did cry, when I found out my mountain of oatmeal was only a dream. Daddy looked at me and said, 'Pumpkins, do you remember Elijah and what God did for him when he needed food?' 'Yes, Daddy, God sent the ravens to feed him.' 'That's right,' said Daddy, 'and the same God lives today and He is able to care for His own. We'll trust Him, shall we Pumpkins?' I was a bit ashamed. I still had Mother and Daddy, and God had not forgotten us. But I was hungry and tired and scared. We knew the enemy would follow us into the jungle, and if they found us they would kill us with their big knives.

"The third day after we left our village we met Juan and several of the other villagers. I don't think I was ever so glad to see anyone in my whole life. They had a few fish and some rice, and we had a regular feast.

"That night we moved on again. I don't know how it happened, but the jungle is thick and mother couldn't hold on to me 'cause we had to go forward one by one in places. Anyway, all of a sudden I was alone. Father had warned me under no circumstance to cry out loud, for the enemy would spot us and we would all be killed. I was the most frightened little girl you ever heard of, Ted.

"I thought I knew which way we had been traveling and I pushed on through the jungle, but I went the wrong way. My dress was torn and I was filthy dirty from head to foot; I was hungry and thirsty; my whole body ached and I wanted to lie down and die. I heard strange sounds in the jungle, sounds I had never heard before. I imagined the enemy was right behind me and I tried to run, but it is not easy to run with thick grasses underfoot and tangled foliage all around one.

"Then I heard a terrible sound. I didn't know what it was at first, but discovered it was the wind blowing a great gale through the trees. I lay flat on the ground, as father had told me to do in case I was ever caught in a windstorm. Then it began to rain. It poured and the ground around me was soaked. I had heard stories of typhoons in the Pacific and I knew I was in the midst of one. The jungle trees, great tall palms, bent almost to the earth. I lay there flat on the ground and I prayed. I prayed, Ted, like I had never prayed before in my life.

"After a while the wind let up and the rain stopped, but I couldn't get up. I just stayed there on the ground. I guess I must have gone to sleep, for when I opened my eyes, it was light. I looked around and not far from where I lay sat a little man with his knees drawn up under his chin and his head down on his knees. He had on a pair of old white trousers, with a bright sash around his waist and the biggest knife I have ever seen, in his belt. I tried to push myself into the ground. Oh, how I wished the earth would swallow me up. ' Dear heavenly Father,' I prayed, 'You have saved me from the storm and You haven't let me starve in the jungle; please, O God, help me, now.' For Jesus' sake.'

"And just then I heard the sweetest music I ever expect to hear this side of heaven. I couldn't believe my ears. The little man was humming. He was humming a tune I knew. It was a chorus we sang nearly every Sunday at the mission. After he had hummed it through once, he started to hum again and I just couldn't help it, I started to sing:

> 'Safe am I; safe am I,
> In the hollow of His hand.'

"When I started to sing, he turned around real quick and I saw that it wasn't a man at all. It was old Juan's grandson. I think he was about fourteen years old. He came to the mission all the time, and he really and truly loved the Lord Jesus with all his heart.

"He told me that Daddy and some of the other men were out looking for me, and that Mother and the women and children were safe on the other side of the river, where the enemy couldn't reach them. I asked how we would cross the river, but all he would say was, 'You wait and see. 'Tis wonderful what God provides for those who trust in Him.'

"It took us only a short while to get to the river, and there we found a raft. And what do you think it was made of?"

"I know, 'cause you told me last time when you told me this story," said Ted. "And you and Juan's grandson got on the raft and he poled you across the river, and there were Mother and Daddy and the other people. And Daddy and Mother hugged and kissed you, and Daddy had all the people bow in prayer, while he thanked God for bringing you back safely. And then what, Nan?"

"It seems to me you know the story well enough to tell it yourself, Teddy."

"Oh, but I want you to tell it to me. You were very hungry and you didn't have anything to eat—"

"That's what I thought, but old Juan's grandson said, 'The boat has carried us over the river away from our enemies, and now let's eat it.' And that's just what we did. For you see the raft was made of coconuts that had been tied together. Someone, we don't know who, had left it in the river.

"Juan's grandson took his big knife and cut open the coconuts, and we drank the milk and ate the meat. How good it tasted! It made us feel well and strong.

"Then we walked on toward the sea, and not long afterward things happened just as Dad had hoped and prayed they would. We met some of Uncle Sam's seamen. They had canoes on the shore and rowed us out to a submarine and we were taken away from that island where the cruel enemy was waiting to destroy us.

"Just three more weeks, Teddy boy, and you and Mother and I will join Daddy in Mindanao and I'll show you the place where we went across on the raft. And I'm going to tell everyone on that island that the Lord Jesus is just like that raft; He'll carry them from death to life, if they'll only trust Him. All I had to do was step on the raft and it carried me away from the enemy to safety. Then we ate our raft and it was food and drink for us; and the Lord Jesus is food and drink for all who hunger and thirst after righteousness."

"Say, Nan, you're a good preacher."

"No, Daddy's the preacher in our family, but I do hope I'll be a good missionary. I can hardly wait to get back to the dear island people. You'll love them, Teddy."

"I know which one I'll like best—old Juan's grandson. And you know why, don't you, Nan?"

—Aunt Theresa

5

KOREA

CHEM'S BICYCLE
✦✦✦✦✦✦✦✦✦✦✦✦✦✦✦✦✦✦✦✦✦

R AT-TAT-TAT, rat-tat-tat," went the ironing clubs in the hands of Chem and his mother as they pounded the white gown wrapped around the stick.

"Washing, spreading clothes on the grass, beating them smooth, sewing the clothes together again, over and over," sighed Chem, his arms aching "Aren't we done yet?"

"No, the gown isn't smooth and glossy enough for the master," replied Chem's mother, who was servant in the home of a magistrate in Seoul, capital of Korea.

"Tell me about the village where you lived when you were little, then I'll forget how tired I am," said Chem, and his black eyes brightened.

"I never saw anything so pretty as the country around our village. I hope you'll see it some day, Son." His mother's tired face looked young again as it had when his father was alive.

"We'll live there!" Chem stopped pounding to smooth back glossy black hair.

"Far away the mountains look purple. When it starts to get dark, blue shadows nestle around them. The slopes are green with all kinds of trees. The rice fields are laced with water when the bright green shoots cover the valleys.

After the rice is harvested, the fields are golden with stubble. The air is clear, and not full of smoke and smells as it is here. You can breathe that air like sweet perfume. It doesn't make you choke and cough as this air does with the smoke of cooking fires." His mother coughed and gasped.

Chem wanted to help her so much, but he had to keep on pounding the gown so no one would notice she had stopped.

"Some day I'll take you to your village!" Chem promised.

"It is too late for me, but you must go as soon as you can, Son!"

In another month Chem's mother was dead. He was alone. No matter how hard he tried, he couldn't please the head servant. "You eat more'n you work!" He slapped Chem until tears rolled down over his high cheek bones.

Chem thought all day and dreamed at night of the village of his mother. "That way is Kimo." He remembered her pointing toward the rising sun. Several times Chem tried to run away from the magistrate's house, but each time he was brought back, and lashed until his skin was raw.

"I'll keep on trying until I do," Chem sobbed.

One day when the cook took Chem to market to carry the heavy basket of vegetables, he stopped to talk to a friend in front of a stall where cabbage was sold. Chem laid down the basket, slipped past the pile of cabbages, through the jostling crowd, and down the road, past the old wall, dodging in and out between donkeys, horses, carts, and people. He walked in front of a man carrying a rack of pottery tied to his back. Thinking he heard the cook's shouts back of him he hurried faster until he was out in the country. The sun was high and he didn't know which way to go, so he kept going with the most people.

"My feet are getting tired!" said Chem, sitting down under a blooming tree to rest. He breathed deeply of the air and found it sweet. Bees buzzed past his head going back and forth to the blossoms.

"The mountains do look purple," he thought, wondering how long it would take him to walk that far. "I'm hungry," he thought; but soon fell asleep.

When Chem awoke with a start, he saw blue shadows gathering around the mountains. Farmers were walking across the fields, looking like moving straw stacks, taking straw home to the village for cooking fires, and so their floors would be warm to sleep on. "I'm more hungry than when I went to sleep! How can I get something to eat?" His brown hands clasped, Chem ran across the field toward the farmer. "I'm a strong boy," he began. "I'll help you gather and carry straw for my supper!"

The farmer grunted, shaking his head, "Too many mouths to feed now!"

Chem felt lonely for his mother. His feet dragged in the dust, as he got on the road again. He walked on and on until he could no longer see the mountains, or even the fields. Feeling very empty, he found a grove of trees, curled up under one and went to sleep, scared of the odd night sounds around him.

When Chem awoke his head felt light and his mouth dry. He drank from a stream and chewed some grass, but still felt dizzy as he walked down the road. How far the mountains are! he thought. Chem passed through a village of thatch roofed houses, red with drying peppers. People stared curiously. Dogs snapped at his heels. His mouth watered at the smell of food in the market.

He saw an old man squatted behind baskets of green and red peppers, smoking his long pipe, the bowl of which rested on the ground. "Can I earn a little food or money by helping you?" Chem asked timidly, remembering the farmer of the night before.

The man stared from beady eyes sharp in his wrinkled face. "Sort this basket of peppers! Put good ones here. Bad ones there!"

Chem worked eagerly, the smell of the peppers making his mouth water more than ever. When he was through, the man handed him a handful of sweet peppers and started to question him. Afraid, Chem thanked him and left, munching the peppers.

The road was steeper than the day before. There were fewer carts and people on it. Chem had to rest more and more. His feet felt so heavy he could scarcely lift them. "My head is so light it feels as if it's going up in the air away from me!"

When blue shadows came up the mountains again, Chem thought he was no closer to them. His heart sank. Why not close my eyes and give up, he thought. "Where's Kimo?" He curled up under a tree, near the edge of a village, perched on the hill, overlooking a valley of yellow rice stubble. On the slope above him, Chem glimpsed a vegetable garden. He saw a man with white skin, short hair, and dressed like a foreigner, come into the garden with a basket. Chem hid behind the tree, watching him. The man picked some red tomatoes, and then turned toward a house which Chem hadn't noticed. There were three houses together, and different from any he had ever seen.

As soon as the man walked away, Chem crawled on his stomach toward the garden, picked a handful of tomatoes, and was gliding back to his hiding place, when he felt a hand on his back. Looking up he saw the white man, who said in careful Korean, "Son, why didn't you ask me for the tomatoes?"

Frightened, Chem dropped the tomatoes. "I'm hungry!" he gasped.

No one but his mother had ever looked at him so kindly.

Chem stood and bowed, but his knees buckled under him, and he almost fell in a faint into the arms of the man, who put down the basket, and carried him into the house.

When he came to, Chem was in a room different from any he had ever seen. The same man and a lady smiled at him: "You are better. Eat this."

The lady fed Chem spoonfuls of steaming broth. Chem could feel it all the way down into his stomach. He felt strong and well again.

After he finished the soup, the man said, "What's your name, and where do you come from?"

"Chem! I walked from Seoul!"

"That is very far, Chem. Tell us about it."

Chem studied the man and woman and fear left him. He told them of his mother, her village, the cruel head servant, and running away. When he was through, the man said, "How would you like to go to school and work here?"

Chem gulped: "I'm poor. Why should you help me?"

"We serve Jesus and He loves and wishes to help all."

"Is He your Master?" asked Chem.

"Yes, our Master and God!" answered the man, taking a small book from his pocket. "This is a New Testament which tells the story of Jesus' life on this earth. You will learn to read it for yourself, but in the meantime we'll teach you more of Him, and you'll learn to love Him."

Chem thought he was dreaming. But the man continued: "I'm Dr. Winslow. This is my wife. We came from far across the seas because we love Jesus and want others to know Him, too. We have a school, church, and hospital here where sick people get well. You will help me in the hospital when you're not busy at school."

"Thank you; thank you," answered Chem.

"Now you must sleep," the lady smiled, patting his head, reminding Chem of his mother.

In the days, weeks, and months that followed, Chem worked in the hospital, learning to do many things which helped Dr. Winslow. He went to school and was learning to read and write. That was often hard, but not so hard as learning to ride the bicycle. "If you'd learn to ride you could go out on calls and deliver medicine much faster," said the doctor. "You could ride to Kimo. You could serve Christ better."

Every time the doctor said, "Now let me show you," perspiration broke out on Chem. He felt as if he were going to pitch headlong into the dusty road. "All you need is confidence that you can ride," said Dr. Winslow. "Just because the first time you crashed into that peddler's cart, you musn't be scared. Now you know how to steer and to use the brake."

Chem couldn't read much of the Bible for himself yet, but he had heard stories of Jesus and could sing all the hymns. "I want to go up to the altar on Consecration Sunday," said Chem, "but first I must get over my fear of riding the bicycle. I've prayed about it and tried, but I haven't faith enough yet to do it. The evil spirits still have hold of me."

"Not evil spirits. You are just scared because of the accident," comforted Dr. Winslow. "We'll try again tomorrow." At the thought of sitting up on the bicycle, Chem felt sick. Just then a woman rushed into the hospital, crying, "My husband and children die of the black sickness!"

Dr. Winslow grabbed his medicine case and spun away on his bicycle, with Chem and the woman running after him. When they arrived at her house, at the edge of the village, Dr. Winslow was busy. "Chem, I haven't enough serum to save all their lives. We need more, quickly, as many other people may be getting sick. The closest is at the mission hospital at Kimo." He pointed up the mountain.

Chem went white. He knew the doctor was needed here. Chem couldn't take time to go back to the school and get one of the other boys who could ride. He must go, but at the thought of the bicycle, his heart pounded against his ribs. "I'll go!" he murmured. His tongue felt stiff. "Pray for me!"

"Remember, 'I can do all things through Christ which strengtheneth me,' " replied the doctor.

Chem didn't know he was praying aloud as he climbed on the bicycle. At first it wobbled, but soon he gained speed, forgetting fear and the narrow, dark roads, only knowing he must hurry. "Kimo, mother's village," he kept thinking. The last slope was so steep he had to push the bike. Out of breath he arrived at the hospital, got the serum, and started back, with hardly a glimpse of the village he wanted to see all his life. Down the slopes he flew, thinking, "God, help me to hurry and save lives."

When he got back Dr. Winslow met him at the door. He shook Chem's hand, "God be praised!"

Chem flashed white teeth. "I'll be at the altar on Consecration Day! Any bicycle riding you want done call on me."

"As soon as I can you shall have a bicycle of your own; then you can go to Kimo and really see it!"

Chem beamed.

—*Esther Miller Payler*
Reprinted by permission of Sunday School Times

ROBERT RICHARD MURDOCK III.
❋❋

ROBERT RICHARD MURDOCK III was patrol boy on the corner of Jackson and Elm. He was named Robert Richard Murdock III because his father was Robert Richard Murdock II, and his grandfather was the first Robert Richard Murdock, His mother always called him Robert, but his Dad just called him R. R. Dad said it could stand for Robert Richard or railroad. Of course he was just teasing. To the boys and girls in his neighborhood and at school, he was plain Bob. I guess I don't need to tell you that that was the name he liked best.

There wasn't much in this country, or any other country for that matter, that Bob wasn't interested in. Every moment of every day of his life he was busy. Sports took up most of his time. If he wasn't playing ball himself, he was reading about some big-league ballplayer. I don't believe there was another twelve-year-old boy in his town who knew more about the players in the major league than Bob Murdock. As for football, he picked the All-American team long before anybody else and he didn't do a bad job of it either. If the Cubs, his favorite baseball team, didn't play a good game, he was blue as could be, and if Northwestern, his father's college, won you'd think Bob had played on the team himself. He'd jump around the living room like crazy when a touchdown was made or a base stolen.

But of all the athletes that Bob held dear, there was no one that came near Gil Dodds. He had seen him run at the Chicago Stadium, and since then Gil Dodds had been his idol. He dreamed what Gil Dodds would do in the great Olympics and even bragged a bit, I'm afraid, to the boys he played with. So when Gil Dodds didn't get to run in the Olympics because of a bad leg, Bob's heart was broken, absolutely broken. Even when he heard Gil Dodds give his testimony from the Youth for Christ Conference at Winona Lake, Indiana, it didn't heal his big hurt. Gil Dodds made it very clear that he believed "all things work together for good to them that love God, to them who are the called according to His purpose." When Bob heard Gil Dodds say that, he just set his Scotch chin in a stubborn line and said, "That's something I can't understand— a swell fellow like him not getting to run in the Olympics. How can that work for good, I'd like to know?"

Mother tried to explain, "There are some things we can't understand, Robert, at the time they happen, but later God shows us just why they happened as they did. Even if God doesn't ever show us, we can trust Him. You know His way is the right way; His way is the best way."

But Bob was hurt and stubborn, "I still don't see how Gil Dodds can say, 'All things work together for good to them that love God.' I don't care, though, he's still the greatest athlete living. I don't care what anybody says." Bob's faith in God's Word was a bit shaken, but he still had his hero way up top. Gil's great love for the Lord Jesus Christ and his boldness to make it known had made a deep impression upon Bob, for he too loved the Lord Jesus.

Up to this time Bob had just taken for granted that the

Bible is God's Word and hadn't given it too much thought. But now every once in a while when he had a moment to himself, he would think about that verse, "All things work together for good to them that love God, to them who are the called according to His purpose." "I can't see it," he'd say to himself. "Gil Dodds could have gone across and, boy, O boy, would he have showed those fellows how to run! Then more people would have listened to him tell about Jesus."

Now summer was over, and Bob was again patrolling the intersection at Jackson and Elm. He was a very careful patrol boy. Last year he had received a medal from the mayor himself. Without anyone knowing it, a committee had observed the different patrol boys and had found Bob to be the most alert and the one who showed the most concern and the greatest kindness toward younger children. He also had a way of making the older boys and girls toe the mark.

School had been in session two weeks when the accident occurred. One minute it seemed he was wearing his brown gabardine trousers with the brown and white striped tee shirt, with his patrol equipment, and the next minute he was lying in a white bed with a silly nightshirt on, and his leg was strung up in front of him looking like it had been cut off that marble statue in Lincoln Park. It really wasn't a minute though; it was two days later.

Bob opened his eyes and looked around the room. He thought to himself, "Where am I? In bed in a strange room." And then he saw a woman all in white standing by the window, "Hey, where am I?" he called.

A pretty nurse turned quickly, and smiling at him she said, "Well, well, so you're awake at last. You're in the Children's Hospital."

"How'd I get here?" Bob was too tired to wait for the answer; he drifted off to sleep, but after a bit he awoke and again he asked, "Say, how'd I get here?"

"You didn't walk in, I can tell you that. A big car, I suppose the biggest one you've ever ridden in, brought you here," said the nurse.

Bob wasn't thinking too clearly and he said, "A hearse?"

"Mercy, no. You're not dead. You were brought here in an ambulance. A car struck you while you were on patrol duty."

"Some patrol boy I turned out to be. Can't even keep out of the way of cars myself. I guess the mayor will take my medal back," said Bob.

"Indeed he won't. I wouldn't be surprised if—" began Miss Thorne, but she didn't finish what she was saying, for Bob burst in, "Oh, I'm just beginning to remember things. A little girl with a yellow dress didn't stop when I gave the signal. She came right out into the street and that guy was coming so fast in the car. Did I get her, Nurse? Did I get her?" Bob was getting excited and his voice was shrill. "Did I get her or did he run her down?"

Miss Thorne laid a cool hand on Bob's head as she said in a quiet voice, "You got her, Bob. You threw her to the side of the street out of the way of the car. She was only hurt a tiny bit, but your leg and head were injured. You're going to be fine, though. Dr. Nystrom, one of our best doctors, set the bone in your leg and everything is going to be just fine."

"That's what you think," thought Bob. He wasn't thinking about the accident; he wasn't thinking about his injured leg. He could think of only one thing. "I don't care what the Bible says. I knew it and this just goes to prove it. All things *do not* work together for good."

You see, without anybody at home knowing it, Bob had taken on a great responsibility. He had promised the big sum of twenty-five dollars to a missionary in China. A couple of weeks before, a letter from a missionary in China was read in the Junior Department. It told of Cheng

Fu, a brave Chinese boy, who loved the Lord Jesus Christ. He loved Him so dearly that he refused to worship his ancestors, and his father had beaten him and thrown him out of the home. He was bruised and sick and weak when one of the missionaries had found him lying beside a building on a crowded street in one of the big cities of China. He was in need of medicine and other things.

Miss Crawford, the Junior superintendent, said that the department was already doing all it could at the present time, but she wanted the children to pray for this Chinese boy. She gave the children the name and address of the missionary, asking them to write to her if they cared to.

That night Bob did some deep thinking. He, Robert Richard Murdock III, would do something for that boy in China. So he had written a letter to the missionary to tell her that he would be sending twenty-five dollars to help Cheng Fu. Bob felt sure that God wanted him to do this. And now he was lying here in a hospital with a broken leg. As he lay there he thought, "The missionary will think that I'm just a bragger, and there won't be any money for Cheng Fu to get the medicine he needs to get well."

It seemed as though the Evil One was right beside his bed all the time whispering to him, "Ha, ha, they tried to make you believe that all things work together for good, didn't they? Silly, isn't it? Here you are with a broken leg and your Mom and Dad will have to use every cent they've saved for the new car to pay the doctors and hospital."

Bob tried to hush the voice of the Evil One, but every day he spoke to him; and at nights, when Bob could not sleep, he'd lie awake and it seemed as though the devil was right there in the room with him. "Wanted to help a little boy, 'way over in China, didn't you? Now you can't even help yourself. Twenty-five dollars is a lot of money for a boy to promise."

Bob would talk back to him, "But I knew I could get it. I didn't promise to give it all right away. I was going to clerk in Tony's grocery store after school, and I was going to save my allowance. And I always get some money for my birthday. That's the first part of November."

Then the voice would say, "Big ideas! I guess I put a crimp in them for you, didn't I? 'All things work together for good.' Silly idea! Twenty-five dollars is a lot of money, Bob, for a twelve-year-old boy to give away. Are you sure God wanted you to do that?"

"Yes, I'm sure." Then Bob began to doubt a bit. "Maybe God didn't want me to help Cheng Fu. Maybe just big people should send money and not kids like me." But he never let the devil know what he was thinking.

The doctors and nurses knew that Bob should be getting better, but he wasn't. Really by this time he should be well enough to have his friends visit him. But he seemed so restless and his temperature would flare up and then go down. And he wasn't at all the cheery boy he used to be. He'd lie for hours just staring into space. When mother asked him what he was thinking about, he'd answer, "Just thinking."

Finally wise, old white-haired Dr. Carter said, "I believe there's something bothering the lad. If we could just find out what it is, maybe he would get well faster." So one day, after Bob had been in the hospital some time, Dr. Carter sat beside his bed and started talking to him. He talked about football, but Bob didn't get a bit excited when the doctor told of the wonderful football team Northwestern had. Dr. Carter talked about pets, but Bob wasn't too interested even when Dr. Carter showed him a picture of his thoroughbred collie that had taken a blue ribbon in the dog show in Chicago. Then Dr. Carter started to talk about traveling and just happened to mention that he had been in China. Bob's eyes lit up. "Is it a big country, sir?"

"Very big, my boy. There are millions and millions of people there."

"It wouldn't be possible that you had met a boy named Cheng Fu there, would it?"

"I met lots of boys with that name. Do you have a friend there with that name?"

"Well, he isn't exactly my friend. I thought he was going to be, but I guess I failed him, and he won't ever be now." And then without realizing what he was doing Bob told the whole story. He told of hearing the letter read from the missionary and of his promise to send twenty-five dollars to China. He told Dr. Carter about how he could never believe again that all things work together for good. He even told Dr. Carter something he had never told anybody else. He told him that he was going to China as a missionary himself some day, if the Lord let him. Dr. Carter stood up and looked him in the eye and said, "Don't let man or devil talk you out of it, boy. China needs you. I know. I've been there and seen her need."

As Dr. Carter stepped into the corridor he met Dr. Nystrom. "Dr. Nystrom, I don't believe we need to wait any longer to have the little party we've been planning. The patient is ready for it. I believe it will make our patient entirely well."

"Yes, sir. Would tomorrow at two be all right?" asked Dr. Nystrom.

"That would be fine," said Dr. Carter.

The next day at two o'clock Bob lay in his bed looking at his broken leg. It sure looked funny sticking up in the air like that. But he wasn't thinking of his leg. He had a sad, far-away look in his eye. If only he could believe that all things work together for good or if he could just say to Satan when he came around putting ideas in his mind, "See, the Bible is true." But there wasn't any way he could possibly earn twenty-five dollars, not for a long time.

The doctors thought he'd be laid up the biggest part of the winter.

Just then Miss Thorne, his nurse, opened the door and said, "Would you like to have some visitors, Bob?"

He was about to say, "I don't care," when he saw the principal of his school, Mr. Matthews, standing in the doorway holding the hand of a little girl dressed in yellow.

"Why, that's the little girl who ran out in the street," thought Bob. And there was his teacher, Miss Clark, and Ronnie Miller and Bud Myers. Boy, there was a whole crowd of people.

They all came into his room and Mr. Matthews stepped right over to the bed. Bob didn't get everything he said, but it seemed as though they thought he was a hero. Mr. Matthews was putting a medal on his nightshirt, and the little girl in the yellow dress was handing him a leather billfold, and the fellow with the camera made him and the little girl both hold on to it until he got the picture for his paper. What was the principal saying? "And, Bob, you are to do whatever you wish with the two hundred and fifty dollars in that wallet. How about a motor scooter?"

"Oh, no, sir. It's for Cheng Fu in China. Every bit of it." That didn't sound like the voice of a sick boy. When Mr. Matthews was telling his wife about the visit to the hospital he said, "The kid said something about 'all things do work together for good' and he looked all lit up as he said it. I don't know what he was talking about, do you?"

"No, I don't," replied his wife. How could they know? They seldom went to church and never read the Bible.

But Bob's mother heard what he said, and when the others had left the hospital she talked very frankly with her boy. "Robert, who is Cheng Fu, and why did you say that about all things working together for good when the principal gave you the money?"

"Mom, I promised to give twenty-five dollars to Cheng

Fu so he could get medicine to get well. When I got hit by the car I thought all my chances of earning the money were over, and I didn't believe God's Word that all things work together for good.' "

"Didn't you know that your father and I would help you if you needed us?" asked Mother.

"Oh, Mom, I thought you and Dad might not like it because I broke my leg and you had to spend lots of money for the hospital and nurses and wouldn't be able to get the new car."

"Why, son, we never realized you were worrying about money. We were so concerned that you get well. That's all we wanted. If I had known you were worried, I would have told you about the settlement. The fact of the matter is, the man who struck you was heavily insured and the insurance company is paying all the expenses and giving you three hundred and fifty dollars beside."

"Boy, I sure know now that everything, even a broken leg, works together for good to them that love God, and to them who are the called according to His purpose. Say, Mom, I love God an awful lot, and you might just as well know that I'm one of the called too. God has called me to China and I'm going. O.K.?"

And Mom, with tears of joy in her eyes, said, "O.K., Robert."

—Aunt Theresa

7

CANADA

THE LONG TRAIL
❖❖❖❖❖❖❖❖❖❖❖❖❖❖❖❖❖❖❖❖❖❖

LOUIS shivered. There it came again—a long, quavering howl of the timber wolf. As the sound slid off into a whine, another wolf answered. Several more replied through the icy Canadian air. A tear almost escaped, but Louis brushed it aside in a hurry. He didn't dare let himself admit he was afraid.

Louis looked around at the poorly made camp. The faithful huskies were a few feet away in a small grove of trees, busy licking their bleeding feet, cut by sharp rocks and icy paths. The dogs pricked up their ears at the wolf howls and whimpered.

Three days of running was almost the limit. This must be Wednesday. But last Monday seemed a hundred years away. On Monday Louis' uncle Ed had fallen through an air hole in the closely packed snow of a glacier and had been badly hurt on the ice beneath.

Louis could still hear the sickening thud of the body striking many feet below, and the terrible groans and curses of the wounded man. The boy dropped a rope made of dog harness and watched his uncle struggle to fasten it under his arms. Then Louis urged the dogs and helped them pull him to the surface of the ground.

Although he was only twelve, Louis gathered all his strength and half carried, half dragged his uncle to the light sled and rolled him into it. The man fainted several times while trying to give himself first aid. One arm was limp, but finally they managed to tear the sleeve off and set the bone. Once that was done, Uncle Ed became unconscious again.

Louis lifted his voice to God. "Oh, Lord, I know Uncle Ed says he hates You, but he doesn't know You. You promised to never leave me, and I need You right now. Hold off the wolves and get us safe home. I know I'm saved, but Uncle Ed isn't. And I want You to save him."

As Louis raised his head, he saw his uncle watching him. Cursing fiercely, the man said, "If you think I'm going to turn coward to God now, you're crazy! I never needed Him before, and I don't need Him now." Gasping in pain, he stopped and then said more softly, "We've got to hit for home. Watch me. I'll get us there."

Uncle Ed had grit. Louis had to admit that. The wolves had seemed to smell the blood afar off and were soon on the trail of the two travelers. On the second day a large pack was gaining on the tired dogs when they topped a ridge.

"Gun!" groaned Uncle Ed, and Louis slipped the heavy rifle from its sheath and knelt before the groaning marksman. "Steady." The boy braced himself as best he could. His uncle shifted a bit, aimed, and pulled the trigger.

The rifle, resting across Louis' shoulder, cracked. Far down the hill a wolf leaped high, then started spinning in circles, biting at the bleeding wound that the bullet had made. Louis turned away from the sight of the rest of the pack, maddened by the sight and smell of blood, springing upon their partner. One after the other the rifleman picked off seven of the gray beasts before he dropped his hand from the rifle and motioned Louis away.

Slipping the gun back into the sheath, Louis cut the whip in the air above the huskies, and they were off.

Twice more that day they stopped and picked off some of the wolves to slow them down. Each time the starving animals stopped to eat one of their own pack, the man and the boy gained that much time.

When night fell, Louis tied the dogs close and kept two fires going. He could hear snarls and saw eyes reflecting in the fire light.

Between the fires, with the dogs near and the wolves eager for his flesh, Louis knelt beside his sleeping uncle Ed and talked again to God. "Show Uncle Ed that You can save us, Lord," he said. "I'm trusting in You. You saved me from sin. It it's Your will, save us from the wolves.

Suddenly Louis awoke. He had fallen asleep while praying. The fire was almost out. Staggering to his feet, he grabbed some of the wood out of the snow and threw it on the embers. As the sparks shot up, several dark forms darted from the circle of light. Fiercely, Louis fed the fires until they blazed high again.

All night Louis fought sleep.

He watched his dogs through bleary eyes. These horrible days—three years were more like it. He couldn't stand another hour of it. He caught his uncle's eyes. The man was too weak now to speak. Louis leaned near.

"It isn't far," the man whispered. "Dump me off. Throw away everything. Strip the sled and you can outrun them. I can't last anyway."

Louis shook his head. "No. God will get us both in safe." But inside of him his heart cried out, "How can He?"

"You little fool," hissed his uncle. Louis felt the man's eyes upon him as he took out the gun and laid the barrel across the sled. Carefully he aimed and squeezed the trigger. A wolf silently dropped, and its companions leaped upon it for their breakfast. A second shot, another fell.

It was the last bullet. Louis dropped the gun to the ground. Swiftly he whipped and coaxed the dogs into their harness. Then he stripped everything from the sled, putting just a few hunks of meat into his pockets.

The older man drew a deep breath and ordered in a fierce whisper, "Put me off!"

The only answer was a shout and the crack of the whip as Louis pushed and the dogs pulled. They were off. This time they had gained only a little distance when the wolves began closing in. Louis didn't know whether he was doing more praying or pushing, but he stumbled on.

Suddenly they topped a rise. From there the trail went down, down, down, all the way to a patch of cabins with smoke pouring from their chimneys. Hope sprang up in Louis' heart. The sled started down the path. The boy raced behind it, praying that they might stay in the track. The runners hissed over the snow, striking fire on hidden pebbles. Their speed carried them over several rises, and they hurtled on downward.

Dragging his heavy leather boots and leaning heavily to this side or that, Louis forced the sled to remain upright around whistling curves. Once, turning his head, he saw the gray shapes bounding far behind.

Heavily the right runner struck a half-hidden rock. The sled careened crazily to one side, rocked for a moment and jumped from the path into some snow drifted over thick bushes.

Dazed, Louis stumbled to his feet, trying to catch his breath. There was no sound from his uncle. The boy's fingers trembled as he set about untangling the traces. Very close he heard a low snarl. Less than a hundred yards off came the leaders of the pack, while the slower ones were strung back up the hill.

The animals slowed, then started to close in—carefully at first, then bolder. In a matter of minutes one would spring on him. It would be all over. If he only had just one bullet—he snatched off the bulky gloves and felt his pockets. There was nothing but one piece of meat and his long-bladed hunting knife.

There was the answer!

Louis made several cuts in the meat with the knife. Then he struck the blade into a chink in the sled and snapped the blade. He did it again, and then the third time. Forcing the pieces of sharp steel into the meat, he threw it at the closest wolf, who snatched it and started to chew.

In a moment the leader's mouth was bleeding from several cuts. The snarling pack, smelling the blood, was upon him.

Mustering his remaining strength, Louis urged the dogs and the sled back to the trail. Clinging to it, he felt his heart lift as they gained speed. Racing away from the pack of wolves, they soon reached the cabins.

Villagers told Louis later that they found him lying beside the sled in the snow close to the village. Someone had lifted him, while other friendly folks cut the cords holding his uncle to the sled. Carefully they carried them both inside and laid them on the bed.

Before long Louis woke to find himself wrapped in blankets in a cheerful, log room. A fire blazed in the stone fireplace. He turned his head to see his uncle lying on the bed on the other side of the room. Slipping out from the blankets, he went to kneel at the man's side.

"Thank You, Lord Jesus, for saving us. And take good care of Uncle Ed. Help him to get well and then help him to come to You and be saved. And thank You for telling me how to get away."

As Louis knelt there, he felt a hand on his shoulder. He looked up into his uncle's eyes. "Me, too, Louis. Me, too. Tell Him that's how I feel, too. He brought us this far. I reckon I'll need Him the rest of the way."

—Frank Waggoner, Jr.

8

SOUTH AMERICA

JUNGLE AMBUSH
❖❖❖❖❖❖❖❖❖❖❖❖❖❖❖❖❖❖❖❖❖

FOR two hours the seven men had lain flat on their stomachs in the underbrush. The sun beamed fiercely above them, and the ground steamed. It would be five hours before dark fell and they could move on.

One man would not move on with them. In his left arm was an ugly wound where one of the poison-tipped arrows lodged. Quickly one of the others had pulled out the arrow and dressed it. But the poison was too powerful. Within an hour the man had died.

Henry Fordham, twelve-year-old mascot of the expedition, squirmed. Several bugs were trying to make a meal from his legs. He raised his head and slapped angrily at the insects.

"Down!" commanded his uncle Jack as he shoved the boy backward.

With a soggy thud a long, ugly, black arrow sank into the water-soaked log beside Henry. "They don't miss anything, kid. You've got to keep down."

Sweat broke out on Henry's forehead. That had been close—too close. Carefully he peeked through the bush in front of him. There was nothing there except an almost solid green bank. There wasn't a sound—not a thing to

49

show that there were at least forty blood-thirsty Motilone Indians. But they were there, bent on killing the party of oil men.

And to think I asked for this, thought Henry. I begged Dad to let me come. He could almost see his head shrunken to the size of a man's fist, hanging from a pole in some village in Venezuela, along with his uncle's and the rest of the men's.

Henry's Illinois home seemed very cozy and very far away now. When his uncle had first asked him if he wanted to come on this oil prospecting trip, he hadn't dreamed that he would get to go. But as he talked to his mother and father (with Uncle Jack's putting in a word now and then), they finally had said yes.

Henry had been saved just three years before. He worried a bit about missing church all the time he was gone on the expedition. But Dad had told him, "Every morning you read a chapter in your Bible, Henry. Ask the Lord to teach you what He wants you to know. Remember that we are praying for you back home."

Swiftly the party had come together. They picked up a surveyor in Chicago and an oil man in New Orleans. A guide and several native workers joined them when they landed in Venezuela. Then they set off into the jungle.

Uncle Jack always smiled when Henry invited him to read the Bible with him. "You go ahead, Henry. But me —I'm too busy for that sort of stuff. We've got a lot of work to do." And Henry began to pray every day for Uncle Jack to become a Christian.

Then the Indians had come—suddenly, swiftly. All morning they had kept the white men cornered. As Henry lay on the spongy, seeping ground, he suddenly gave a start. "This is Sunday, isn't it?"

"Yes. But keep down. Oof! Look at that baby."

Henry shivered as he saw a long, poison arrow quivering

in the tree just about four feet away. "It's lucky we've got a river behind us and that clearing in front, or they'd slip up here and we'd be gone. I don't believe we've hit anything all day. You just can't wing shadows."

Henry shook his head. Then, rolling partly on his side, he took a little black Book from his pocket and while thumbing through it, he started to read. For a long time he read and then he rested his head on his arm and prayed silently.

Finally Henry raised his head. "Uncle Jack, will you help me do something?"

"Help you? How?"

"Help me to pray."

"Now listen, Kid," Uncle Jack sounded a little angry. "I told you I didn't go for that stuff. Let me alone. I've got enough on my mind."

"You aren't going anywhere," returned Henry, "unless one of those arrows gets the range. You always said before, that you didn't have time. You don't seem very busy now."

"You win. What do you want?"

"I was just reading where Jesus said that if two of us shall agree about anything that we ask, it shall be done. And if we two would agree that we wanted to get out of this spot, God would hear us—that is, if it's His will."

"Yes?" Uncle Jack's voice went up and hung on the word. "And what is God's will?"

"Well," said Henry, trying to find the right words, "if anything would cause you to accept God's Son as your Saviour, that would be in His will."

"Um-hum." Uncle Jack wiped off his rifle. Then he looked hard at the mass of leaves and branches on the other side of the clearing. Finally he said, "Yeh, that sounds fair enough. I'll tell you what I'll do. We're in a tight spot.

If your God can get us out of here, I'm going to look into this salvation business and see if there's anything in it for me."

"Then we're agreed, aren't we?" asked Henry. "Then we can pray."

"You do the praying for both of us." Uncle Jack took off his pith helmet and wiped the sweat band.

So Henry prayed, and he told the Lord about the tight spot they were in and of the promise that Uncle Jack had made. Then he raised his head and looked Uncle Jack in the eye.

"You watch," he said. "I don't know how He will do it, but He will."

Uncle Jack shook his head. "If those fellows don't get the idea of rushing us before sun-down, we may be able to figure this out ourselves. But if they do, we're through."

The afternoon wore on. The heat grew worse. Several little lizards started taking bites from their legs. One of the natives nearly lost his life. A surprise bite from one of the little animals sent him into the air with a howl. Instantly there were two smacks of arrows, and he lay still.

Carefully Henry looked at the native. He was badly scared, but not hurt. One arrow had taken his helmet off. The other had shattered against the hard rifle stock.

It was so quiet after that, that one of the men thought the Indians had gone. Slowly he raised the surveying glass up into the air. Hardly was it up in the open when an arrow smashed the glass as though a bullet had cut it out. And the second arrow slammed into the wooden stand on which the glass was mounted.

"Don't kid yourself," growled one of the other men. "They won't leave till we're gone."

But Uncle Jack knew the Indians of the Motilone country. "They will leave shortly before sun-down," he said. "They're afraid to be away from their village after dark."

"But before they leave, they may try to rush us and finish us off. They want our heads. We'd look mighty nice, all shrunken and strung up."

"Watch out!" One of the men began to empty his rifle at a moving spot in the jungle. "Here they come!"

From several spots across the clearing dark-skinned men broke forth. They raced toward the white men's hiding place.

Seven rifles cut loose. As quickly as they had come, the wild men were gone again, leaving several Indians groaning on the ground. Perhaps the fire power of the small group had surprised them.

The guide shook his head. "Shells are low," he said.

Henry heard a twig crack noisily, then another. No, that wasn't a twig. It was rifle fire! It couldn't be very far away.

In just a few minutes Henry heard a cry from beyond the clearing. Uncle Jack was answering. Then, across the clearing came a soldier, followed by a band of heavily armed men. They were wearing Venezuela army uniforms.

The leader explained. "We have taken care of your Indians. But, gentlemen, it's a strange story. We're out on patrol. We have to keep our eye on those Indians or they can be pretty nasty. But they're afraid of the army. We have not been here for more than three years. But I felt I should come. So I did."

"Lucky for us that you did," said Uncle Jack. He nodded toward Henry. Henry knew he was thinking of the promise he had made.

"Perhaps when we get back, Henry," the older man said, "you can tell me what I ought to know about salvation."

—*Frank Waggoner, Jr.*

9

MEXICO

THE CHAPEL BELL
****

ANTONIO looked around over the little group of people in the chapel. Lucita was there—his friend. She
loved the stories of Jesus as much as he did. If the chapel
should be closed and the Man of the Mission should go
away, Lucita would be sad. Antonio must not let that happen.

Once the chapel had been crowded. The people had been
eager to hear the stories of Jesus. Now, only a few came
to hear the Man of the Mission. Tony knew why.

The Man of the Mission had told the people again and
again that they must forget their foolish fears and their
superstitions. But the superstitions of Tony's people were
old like the rocks by the mission gate. The stories of
Jesus were new and strange. They were almost too beautiful to believe. One had to say over and over in his heart,
"It is true that Someone cared for me and died for me on
the cross."

Now, the stories that were being told about the silent
bell were crowding out the stories of Jesus.

High in the tower of the mission there was a bell. Every
Sunday morning the Man of the Mission had reached up
his hand and pulled hard on the rope in the little front

hall of the mission. The sound of the bell had carried far over the flat country. All had come when they had heard its silver tones on the warm, lazy air.

But now there was no longer a bell. One day the Man of the Mission had pulled on the rope, and no sound had come.

Teresa, the Wrinkled One, had not liked the Man of the Mission. Before he had come, the people had listened to her. But, afterward, they laughed and cried, "Away, Teresa, Wrinkled One. Away with your silly superstitions. Go to those who have not heard the stories of Jesus."

Teresa had been very angry.

It was Teresa who had cried out in an angry moment that the bell would be silent. Now it was true. Tony's people had heard. They must believe that Teresa knew. They listened once more to her. She said to stay away from the mission.

"As long as the evil spirit is angry, the bell will not ring," she said.

Tony wanted the mission to be filled again that all might hear the beautiful stories. He felt sorrow, too, for the Man of the Mission. But Tony could not tell him why the people did not come. He would be very sad if he knew that Tony's people had given their faith back to the old and wrinkled Teresa.

So Tony asked if he might climb into the tower and see why the bell would not ring.

"Why, Tony?" the Man of the Mission had asked.

Tony had dug his brown toe into the ground. He had not looked up.

"It is sweet to hear on the Sabbath day," he said.

"It is not safe to go there," the man had said. "The wood is old and rotten. The tower is high, and the adobe that covers the wood is cracked and dried. It might not hold your weight."

"I am not afraid," Tony told him. The man had looked at him, but he had not said, "No."

Tony spent much time thinking about the matter. He knew this was a matter for prayer. But he had not learned to pray alone. He went to a place where the sugar cane grew tall. There he got down on his bare knees.

But he didn't know how to go about praying. He stayed there for a long time. When he got up, he knew he was going to climb the bell tower that night. If the evil spirit was up there, Jesus would keep him safe.

Tony could hardly wait for the coming of the night. When he had eaten his beans and corncakes, he took his blanket and went to the corner of his little adobe home.

Soon the Mamacita, his mother, and the Padre, his father, were asleep. Carmelita and Maria, the little sisters, were quiet, too.

Tony crept out of his blanket and slipped through the open door of the little house. The moon had not yet come from behind the Mountain of the Lost Goats. It was so dark that he stumbled in the rough places of the road.

He did not know it was so dark in the night alone. He had never before gone into the darkness without the Padre. But he would not turn back. There were many things to be heard in the night, too—sounds he could not name, small sounds made big in the stillness.

He hoped the Mamacita would not waken and find him gone from his corner. He did not know what she would do. "Please do not let her wake, God in heaven," he whispered. Then suddenly he knew that he had learned to pray.

At last Tony came to the mission. He had to grope his way through the inky darkness of the entrance, to the rickety boards nailed to the wall for a ladder to the bell tower.

"And please don't let it fall," he whispered again.

He tried not to think of the stories Teresa told of the terrible things which happen to those who anger the Evil One. One of the boards broke under his weight, but Tony caught himself. He had never thought it could be so far up to the tower.

Old Teresa was wrong, Tony said to himself again and again as he climbed. He thought of the Man of the Mission and how sure he looked when he said, "God will take care of you."

The door at the top opened easily. All was pitch blackness above. Tony caught his breath and forced himself to go up through the hole.

At the front of the tower was a little window, but it was closed. Tony stumbled toward it. He heard the old wood of the floor of the little room of the bell cracking beneath his weight. If he could find the window—if only it would open and let in a little light. He fought his way through spider webs.

Then he heard something moving softly in the darkness.

For a minute he couldn't move. Then he whispered, "For Jesus."

He made his feet take a few steps forward. His hands groped along the wall until he found the window and the latch. The window creaked open.

A large yellow moon had come over the mountain. It threw a shaft of light into the bell tower. The light fell right across the bell.

As Tony looked, he gasped. Then he began to laugh. It was good to laugh. He laughed until he was no longer afraid of Teresa and her stories of evil spirits.

The bell was half turned over. Peeping from it with startled eyes was a mother opossum. An old rafter from the roof had fallen and caught the bell half tipped. The mama opossum had thought it a fine, quiet place to raise a family.

"You'll have to move out, little one," said Tony as he moved the fallen board. The bell fell straight without a sound, for the clapper struck the soft body of a small, tumbling opossum.

The mother animal looked angry for a moment. Then she slumped off through a hole down the roof with her babies following after her. Tony had only to close the window and make his way back down the rickety ladder.

The moon lit up the road with light almost like day. There was no stumbling on the way home. Tony sang softly as he went along—a song the Man of Mission had taught them. On Sunday his people would be back in the chapel singing it again—at the call of the bell.

How angry old Teresa, the Wrinkled One, would be! But Tony sang a little stronger when he thought of Lucita's smile when she heard the ringing bell.

—Louise Hannah Kohr
Used by permission of My Counselor, and the author.

ABDUL KHAN'S DIAMOND
❖❖❖❖❖❖❖❖❖❖❖❖❖❖❖❖❖❖❖❖❖❖❖❖❖❖❖❖❖

L AST summer I visited my Uncle Pete who teaches a
Missions course in a Bible School on the East Coast.
We were sitting in his office, when I looked out and saw a
dark-skinned boy scrubbing the floor in the corridor.

"Say, he's a swell looking fellow," I said. "But he's got
an ugly scar on his cheek."

"Abdul Khan is a big help around here," said Uncle Pete.
"I'll never forget the first time I saw him in north Arabia.
I was sitting with my back against a palm tree, my sun helmet pushed back on my head. My native helpers were
watering the camels of our caravan. I was just sitting there
thinking how lovely this touch of green was in the midst
of the desert; how refreshing the water was in the midst
of the hot sands.

"I looked up and saw several horsemen galloping toward
us. If you've never seen Arabian horses on a desert
stretch, I don't know whether you can picture how beautiful they are. They're the most graceful horses in the
world and they're swift. They are also intelligent and very
spirited. The riders wore turbans and long, flowing
robes and they were carrying long spears. As the Arabs
drew rein near me, the horses reared back on their hind

legs. Quick as a flash, one man dismounted and walked over to us. He saw that I was an American so he talked in slow but perfect English.

" 'Peace to you,' he said. 'Abdul Khan, son of Hassan Ali, saw the camel train and bade us stop and wish you good day'.

"When I heard the man say Abdul Khan, son of Hassan Ali, I looked up quickly. Abdul Khan was only a boy of twelve, but he was known in all Arabia. His father, Hassan Ali, was one of the richest sheiks in that whole land. He had great herds of sheep and a whole fleet of the fastest Arabian horses in the desert. Hassan Ali also had a thousand fighting men that would draw the sword at his word. It was said he had saddles studded with diamonds, pearls in baskets and other precious stones in caskets in his tents. Hassan Ali was a strict Mohammedan and he knew his holy book, the Koran, from cover to cover.

"I was curious to see a boy who could ride better than any man on the desert, who lifted his hand and a thousand men rode to battle at his bidding, who held his head high and who was afraid of nothing.

" 'Tell the son of your leader, Abdul Khan, that Pete Hanssen of Roseville, U.S.A., whose ancestors were Vikings, bids him welcome.'

"The Arabian who had lighted from his horse to talk to me went to the boy and delivered my message in the beautiful Arabian language. Abdul Khan raised his arm in greeting and talked quickly in Arabic to the man, who turned to me and said, 'Abdul Khan would make speech with you, Pete Hanssen of Roseville U.S.A., whose ancestors were Vikings.' I had been teasing about that Viking part, although my grandparents had come from the land of the Vikings. Abdul Khan had taken it all seriously. So I got serious myself. 'Tell Abdul Khan I would like very much to talk to him.'

" 'He wishes to talk to you privately,' said the man.

" 'Tell him my native helpers are busy with the camels. If he wishes, we can sit under this palm tree and talk. But say, I can't speak Arabic,' I said.

" 'Oh, Abdul Khan speaks well the English language. He was tutored well in that language before he accompanied his father, Hassan Ali, to England,' replied the dark-skinned Arab.

"So Abdul Khan and I sat under a palm tree in the middle of the desert and talked. I had gone to school in the United States and I thought I knew English, but he spoke it much better than I. I guess I stared at the huge diamond ring on his finger, while we were talking, for he held it up to the light and said, in beautiful crisp English, 'There is no finer in all Araby. It is a gem fit for a king. The dark continent of Africa has given the world much beauty and much heartache.' And then I nearly fainted, for he said with a real American twist to his tongue, 'Almost knocks your eyes out, doesn't it?' Who was this boy, son of a sheik, rich, powerful, and proud, who spoke perfect English that could be accepted in the King's court and at the same time knew American slang? Then he told me that during the war some American G. I.'s had been stationed in this part of the world, and he had spent quite a bit of time with them.

" 'When the Americans were here,' he went on to say, 'there was one that nearly everybody laughed at. They called him Preacher, but he told me some things I have never forgotten, and he gave me a book, the like of which I had never before read. Perhaps you are a reader of the Book?' questioned Abdul Khan.

" 'What book do you mean? I've read lots of books,' I said. Although I was almost sure I knew which Book he had in mind.

"Adul Khan came closer and whispered, 'It is the Christian's Bible. I had one but my father in a fit of anger burned it.'

" 'Oh, you mean this Book,' and I took my New Testament out of my pocket.

"Abdul Khan quickly stepped closer to me and hid my hand holding the New Testament under his flowing robe.

" 'I have talked with every American I have seen this last year, since the longing for the Book took hold of me, and you are the first one that had one. Tell me, do you believe in and follow the teachings of the Book?" he asked eagerly.

" 'Abdul Khan, do you mean, am I a Christian and do I believe that the Lord Jesus Christ is the Son of God and that He died for my sins? Indeed I do!'

"His piercing dark eyes lit up with a heavenly light. And he said in deep, reverent tones, 'God be praised. We are brothers. I have found a believer at last.' Then he went on, 'I know that Book must be precious to you, but for it I would give this diamond ring.'

" 'Hold on,' I said. 'You can have it for nothing. I'll get myself another one when I get to headquarters.'

"But Abdul Khan would not take the Book for nothing. He was a proud Arab and he made me take his beautiful diamond ring. I couldn't wear such a valuable ring in the desert—I didn't have a thousand men to protect me from robbers like Abdul Khan had. So I fastened the ring to my undershirt.

"As I handed him the New Testament, he hid it in the folds of his robe, saying, 'God bless you, kind sir. The peace of our Lord Jesus Christ be with you. I shall remember to pray for you that God will bless you in your journey and make you a blessing.' With one leap he mounted his horse, raised his hand in farewell, shouted a command to his men and rode away into the desert. I would have thought it was all a dream, except that my Testament was gone and in my possession was the most beautiful gem I had ever seen.

"Sometimes I'd feel the diamond against my skin as I

rode through the desert and I'd breathe a prayer for Abdul
Khan. I knew if he openly confessed Christ his father
would disown him and he would become an outcast. I just
couldn't imagine Abdul Khan an outcast, having nothing
and with no chance to get anything. The Mohammedans
despised those who reject the Koran as the Holy Book
and those who turn away from Mohammed to Christ. They
hold firm to the belief that there is but one God, Allah,
and Mohammed is his prophet.

"Two years later I happened to be in Mecca, the center
of Mohammedan worship. Pilgrims from all parts of the
Mohammedan world throng to this place, for they believe
they will be specially blessed by coming there to worship
Allah.

"I stopped at one of the stalls in the busy market place
to buy some trinkets to send back home to the folks. As
I stood fingering the stuff I noticed a shabbily dressed
boy, with a deep scar across his dark cheek. He was selling some little books. I walked over to him and he glanced
up. I could not be mistaken—it was Abdul Khan! He was
selling Gospels of John. I couldn't help hugging him right
there on the street, and he hugged me. It was like meeting
a long lost brother.

"He took me to the little mission where he stayed and
we talked far into the night. He told me how he had started
at Matthew, the first chapter in the New Testament,
planning to read it straight through. In chapter 10 he said
he came upon some words that burned into his heart. He
read, 'Whosoever therefore, shall confess me before men,
him will I confess also before my Father which is in heav-
en. But whosoever shall deny me before men, him will I
also deny before my Father which is in heaven.'

" 'After I read that in God's Word, I knew I had to tell
my father, Hassan Ali, that I was a Christian,' said Abdul
Khan. 'I had to tell him no matter what it cost me. My
father flew into a rage and took from me the beautiful

Arabian horse that I dearly loved. But still I did not give up my belief in the Lord Jesus Christ. When my father saw that I would not be changed, he took from me my beautiful clothes and the privileges of a son; he made me as a servant and I was disgraced before the men in my father's household. Then I was beaten and one day angered beyond himself, my father threw his short spear at me, yelling as he did so, "Out of my presence, ungrateful one. You are no son of Hassan Ali!" My mother, at the risk of her own life, helped me to escape. I was often hungry and in much need, but God cared for me.'

"Finally he found Christian missionaries who took him in, but he was poor—poorer than the poorest. Abdul Khan who had ridden the fleetest steed in Arabia and had worn garments fit for a king, who had commanded a thousand men and who had jewels fit for a rajah, had given it all up for love of the Lord Jesus Christ.

"I knew now why I had never sold the diamond ring. I reached inside my shirt and unpinned the ring and said, 'Abdul Khan, hold out your hand; your brother wishes to give you a gift.' And I placed his diamond in his hand.

" 'Thank you, my brother,' was all he said. I found out later that he had been praying for money to come to the United States and study in one of our Bible Schools. He knew and I knew that this was God's way of answering his prayers.

"And that is the story of the dark-skinned boy you saw scrubbing the floors," finished Uncle Pete.

As I looked through the glass at Abdul Khan, who was way down at the end of the corridor by this time, I thought to myself, "Abdul Khan, son of Hassan Ali, the most powerful shiek in Arabia, would never scrub floors, but Abdul Khan, a son of God would." I opened the door a bit and heard him singing as he scrubbed. His voice was deep and clear and the words very distinct, "Great is thy faithfulness, O God, my Father."

—Aunt Theresa